Spring Harvest Bible Workbook

Inseparable
Life in Christ, in the Spirit, and in the World

Romans 8

Contents

About this book

This book is written primarily for a group situation, but can easily be used by individuals who want to study Romans 8. It can be used in a variety of contexts, so it is perhaps helpful to spell out the assumptions that we have made about the groups that will use it. These can have a variety of names – homegroups, Bible study groups, cell groups – we've used group as the generic term.

- The emphasis of the studies will be on the application of the Bible. Group members will not just learn facts, but will be encouraged to think 'How does this apply to me? What change does it require of me? What incidents or situations in my life is this relevant to?'

- Groups can encourage honesty and make space for questions and doubts. The aim of the studies is not to find the 'right answer', but to help members understand the Bible by working through their questions. The Christian faith throws up paradoxes. Events in people's lives may make particular verses difficult to understand. The group should be a safe place to express these concerns.

- Groups can give opportunities for deep friendships to develop. Group members will be encouraged to talk about their experiences, feelings, questions, hopes and fears. They will be able to offer one another pastoral support and to get involved in each other's lives.

- There is a difference between being a collection of individuals who happen to meet together every Wednesday and being an effective group who bounce ideas off each other, spark inspiration and creativity, pooling their talents and resources to create solutions together: one whose whole is definitely greater than the sum of its parts. The process of working through these studies will encourage healthy group dynamics.

Space is given for you to write answers, comments, questions and thoughts. This book will not tell you what to think, but will help you discover the truth of God's word through thinking, discussing, praying and listening.

FOR GROUP MEMBERS

▶ You will probably get more out of the study if you spend some time during the week reading the passage and thinking about the questions. Make a note of anything you don't understand.

▶ Pray that God will help you to understand the passage and show you how to apply it. Pray for other members in the group too, that they will find the study helpful.

▶ Be willing to take part in the discussions. The leader of the group is not there as an expert with all the answers. They will want everyone to get involved and share their thoughts and opinions.

▶ However, don't dominate the group! If you are aware that you are saying a lot, make space for others to contribute. Be sensitive to other group members and aim to be encouraging. If you disagree with someone, say so but without putting down their contribution.

FOR INDIVIDUALS

▶ Although this book is written with a group in mind, it can also be easily used by individuals. You obviously won't be able to do the group activities suggested, but you can consider how you would answer the questions and write your thoughts in the space provided.

▶ You may find it helpful to talk to a prayer partner about what you have learnt, and ask them to pray for you as you try and apply what you are learning to your life.

▶ The New International Version of the text is printed in the book. If you use a different version, then read from your own Bible as well.

Introduction

He had led a pretty sordid and riotous life. He had moved in with his girlfriend aged only seventeen, and even after the birth of their son had numerous affairs before abandoning them altogether[1]. His mother despaired for his welfare and prayed fervently for a change in his life. One day, aged 32, he heard a voice telling him to read. Believing it was God speaking to him, he dug out a Bible and began reading Paul's letter to the Roman Church. Halfway through he knew without a shadow of a doubt that the words he was reading were going to turn his life upside down. In fact they changed not only his life, but the whole world.

It was the fourth century, and in his own words he described his conversion after reading half of Romans like this:

"No further would I read; nor needed I: for instantly at the end of this sentence, by a light as it were of serenity infused into my heart, all the darkness of doubt vanished away."

The convert's name was Augustine, and he went on to be used by God to transform the way that Christians understood their faith, and, throughout his lifetime, to help defend that faith from division and heresy. His writings became "one of the main pillars on which the church of the next 1000 years was built."[2]

Over a thousand years later another young man also began reading Paul's letter to the Romans. Unlike Augustine, he was very familiar with the Bible, having devoted his life as a monk to reading it, and yet there was something about this particular letter that traumatised him every time he picked it up. Eventually it acted as a fuse that triggered him to challenge the corruption and compromise of the institutional church, and to launch a mass movement calling Christians back to faithful biblical Christianity. That young monk was Martin Luther and when he nailed his 95 Theses to the door of a church in Wittenburg, Germany, he started a reformation of the church that would again transform the world.

Romans was also the letter that challenged the theologian, Karl Barth, to his core about the holiness of God. Reading it, he suddenly realised that his faith had been more about appeasing culture than it had about worshipping the living God, and he underwent a radical rewiring of his understanding of God. Because of his powerful spiritual experience through the letter to the Romans, he and his convert and friend Dietrich Bonhoeffer were able to offer a profound resistance to the Nazis during the

1   From: *Journal Of The History Of Sexuality, Volume 11, Number 4, October 2002 pp. 545-569 | 10.1353/sex.2003.0045*
2   Mark Galli, *339 Christians everyone should know*

Second World War, even when facing extreme danger including the certain threat of death.

There is yet a further example of a teenager coming to terms with a huge change in her life. In an instant she had gone from being a vibrant and active girl to a wheelchair-using quadriplegic, after a tragic diving accident in Chesapeake Bay. But this was just the beginning of a lifetime of powerful ministry. For Joni Eareckson, she came to understand her accident in the light of Romans 8, which a friend read to her as she lay in her hospital bed. She grasped that somehow this terrible event fitted in to a 'pattern of good', and this truth transformed her life and gave her a hope that she has passed on to millions of others around the world.

Whether you are well versed in the teachings of the Bible like Barth and Luther, or are reading this book like Augustine or Joni; with very little experience of faith, it is my prayer that you too will experience the life-changing power of the word of God through the letter of Paul to the Romans.

Chapter 8 is arguably both the most comforting and challenging section of Romans; this most magnificent of New Testament letters. In the preceding seven chapters, Paul has built up a strong case for our universal inadequacy before a perfect God. Everything we may rely on to get by in life – our ancestry, our moral standards, our status – is shown to be incapable of removing our fundamental guilt that demands the due punishment of death. In Romans 3, Paul reveals the good news - God has found a way to satisfy his requirements for righteousness by sending his perfect son Jesus into the world to live and to die for everyone pronounced guilty. Through faith, his ultimate sacrifice is available to all; for those who lived thousands of years earlier and for those who live thousands of years later. By trusting in God's promises we too are offered a new identity which absolves our guilt and removes the punishment. This new identity is tied up "in Christ" as we will see. But Paul recognises the need to explore the question – how do we live with this new holy identity in unholy times? How can it inspire us to live radically in our world? How does it help us when we are faced with those all too familiar problems such as guilt, worthlessness, and frustration? Paul has set the scene for the awe-inspiring message in chapter 8 of the work of the Holy Spirit in the life of believers.

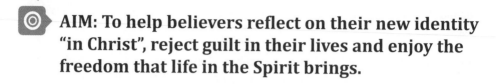

AIM: To help believers reflect on their new identity "in Christ", reject guilt in their lives and enjoy the freedom that life in the Spirit brings.

TO SET THE SCENE

Read out the following story:

Every time Jenny walks home from church she feels more guilty. Those ladies serving coffee looked quite tired and unenthusiastic this morning. And Jenny's bad back meant she wasn't able to help clear away the chairs and the sound system from the school hall that her church used for its services. The preacher had delivered a challenging sermon on devotion to God - again - but so little changed last time she went forward for prayer, she had shrunk down in her seat during this week's altar call. Now she was rushing home before the roast overcooked, realising that she had, once again, failed to invite anybody to share her ample meal. As she arrived at the front door of her house she couldn't get the image of the mission trip video that new young couple had shared out of her head – there was such a contrast between their home and hers. Jenny wonders if she is cut out for the Christian faith, as each week the guilt seems to just mount up.

Split into pairs and discuss:

| **My thoughts and notes....** |

- Can you relate to Jenny in any way? Is there anything you might want to say to help her?

- What causes you to feel most guilty?

READ THE PASSAGE TOGETHER:

8 ¹Therefore, there is now no condemnation for those who are in Christ Jesus, ²because through Christ Jesus the law of the Spirit who gives life has set you free from the law of sin and death. ³For what the law was powerless to do because it was weakened by the flesh, God did by sending his own Son in the likeness of sinful flesh to be a sin offering. And so he condemned sin in the flesh, ⁴in order that the righteous requirement of the law might be fully met in us, who do not live according to the flesh but according to the Spirit.

Romans 8:1-4

My thoughts and notes....

 1. Read verse 1 again. What does the promise of "no condemnation" mean to you? As you read through verses 1-2 what is the condition that this promise is based on?

 2. In verse 1 Paul uses one of his favourite phrases of Romans 8; "in Christ". Another way of expressing this is "in sync with Christ", "inseparable from Christ" or "in union with Christ". Take a look at the following references in Romans and try and explain what being "in Christ" means for believers?

> *In the same way, count yourselves dead to sin but alive to God in Christ Jesus.*
> *Romans 6:11*

> *For the wages of sin is death, but the gift of God is eternal life in Christ Jesus our Lord.*
> *Romans 6:23*

> *For I am convinced that neither death nor life, neither angels nor demons, neither the present nor the future, nor any powers, neither height nor depth, nor anything else in all creation, will be able to separate us from the love of God that is in Christ Jesus our Lord.*
> *Romans 8:38-39*

How does this apply to me?

3. Which of the following illustrations best helps you to understand what being in Christ means? Or can you think of an alternative picture or experience that is meaningful to you?

► My computer has limited resources on its own, but once it is online I have access to all the resources of the web through my internet connection. Similarly by faith we are connected to all the resources that are ours in Christ.

► If I place a plant in the dark it will soon wither and die, but if it is placed in the sunshine it will grow and flourish. Being in Christ is like being placed in his light to allow his goodness to shine on us, nourish us and enable us to thrive.

► When an adopted child moves into their new home, they gain not only new parents, but a new family tree, a new identity and all the resources of their new family. Similarly being in Christ is about being adopted into God's family, and accessing not only his identity, but also his family traits, resources, privileges and responsibilities.

► In the novel *Captain Corelli's Mandolin*[3], the Italian regiment that Corelli commands is put in front of a firing squad to be executed. As the bullets fly through the air, a huge man grabs Corelli and wraps his body around him, shielding him from the gunfire. As a result, the soldier dies but Corelli is saved. Being in Christ means that the punishment that was due for us is absorbed by Jesus instead of us.

---

3   de Bernieres L. (1998) Captain Corelli's Mandolin, Vintage Books

Inseparable: Us in Christ

"If we are 'in Christ', then we are united to him at all points of his activity on our behalf. We share in his death (we were baptised into his death), in his resurrection (we are resurrected with Christ), in his ascension (we have been raised with him), in his heavenly session (we sit with him in heavenly places, so that our life is hidden with Christ in God), and we will share in his promised return."[4]

Sinclair Ferguson, Christian Spirituality

 4. When Paul refers to the law in Romans, he means the old covenant law that God revealed to Moses. Although the law is a good gift from God, it shows up our moral failure, which merits God's punishment, so Paul calls it the law of sin and death. What are the contrasts in verses 1-4 that Paul makes between the Spirit and the law?

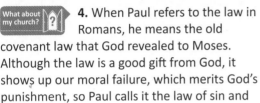 **5.** Which of the following statements best fit with your understanding of the work of the Spirit? Which of the following statements best fit with your experience of the work of the Spirit?

a. Through the Spirit we come to know who Jesus is, and what he has done for us and thus our conversion is a work of the Spirit.

b. Through the Spirit we are empowered to live the Christian life.

c. Through the Spirit we are united with Christ.

d. Through the Spirit the fruit of the Spirit is worked into our characters.

e. Through the Spirit the gifts of the Spirit are operative in our churches today.

---

4 Alexander, D.L. (ed.) (1981) Christian Spirituality: Five Views
   Of Sanctification, Ferguson,S. (1987) from Christian Spirituality:
   Five Views Of Sanctification, Zondervan p.58

The Holy Spirit

The Holy Spirit is fully God.	1 Corinthians 12:4-6
	Matthew 28:18-20
The Holy Spirit is a person.	Ephesians 4:30-31
The Holy Spirit is the Spirit of Jesus.	Galatians 4:6
The Holy Spirit is at work in our conversion.	John 16:8
The Holy Spirit makes us part of the church.	1 Corinthians 12:13
The Holy Spirit empowers us for witness.	Acts. 1:6-8
The Holy Spirit guarantees our future inheritance.	Ephesians 1:13-14
The Holy Sprit produces the character of Christ in us.	Galatians 5:22-25
The Holy Spirit gives gifts to us for the building up of the church.	1 Corinthians 14:12

6. Verse 3 explains that it is because of Jesus' life and death that we can live without guilt or condemnation. How can this help us now as we struggle to live out our faith day by day?

7. Think through the following statements. Are we to counsel all these people with the comforting part of verse 1: "There is no condemnation"? How are we to work this out practically?

"I feel guilty for not exercising my gift of hospitality enough."

"I feel guilty about all those people I hurt when I went off the rails as an unruly teenager."

"I feel guilty about the affair I am currently involved in."

"I feel guilty about spending so much money on a holiday."

"I feel guilty for missing a quiet time this morning."

My thoughts and notes....

8. In light of what we have studied in Romans 8:1-4 how would you revise your advice you gave to guilty Jenny at the beginning of our study? Share with one another things you feel guilty about, and allow others to help you through prayer and encouragement to be released from that guilt.

9. Think of times you have felt arm-twisted or guilt-tripped into an act of service at church or signing up to a church rota. Imagine that you had the job of recruiting new people to help run an evangelistic course or take over the coffee rota. Describe how you could do so in a non-condemning way.

My thoughts and notes....

REFLECT

No condemnation now I dread;
Jesus, and all in him, is mine;
Alive in him, my living Head,
And clothed in righteousness divine.
Bold I approach the eternal throne,
And claim the crown through Christ, my own.[5]

DURING THE WEEK

One way we value what Christ has done for us is to try and remember where we would have been without him. Why not try and reflect on what it means to you that you are no longer condemned by God because of your moral guilt before him. Some of us feel guilty all the time. We feel guilty about slowing the traffic down when we cross a road. We feel guilty when putting our kids to bed for having felt cross with them earlier. We feel guilty for having no spare change when we pass by a charity collector and we feel really guilty about accepting a second helping of dessert at dinnertime. Others of us rarely feel guilty, and can easily knock into someone in the supermarket and not think to apologise, or help ourselves to a drink at work without offering one to those around us. Whichever category we are in, let's try this week to redress the balance. Recognise pangs of guilt or pricks of conscience not to feel bad about ourselves, but to encourage us to think of others. Bring our failings to God and worship and thank him for his gift of forgiveness and freedom from condemnation.

---

5 'And Can It Be That I Should Gain', Charles Wesley 1707-1788

FOR FURTHER STUDY

Romans 8 is such a powerful passage - you might like to set yourself a target of trying to memorise it in chunks over the course of the studies we are going to do together. Alternatively you might want to try and memorise one or two verses from each of the five passages we are going to look at.

This week try and memorise either Romans 8:1, or verses 1-4

Therefore, there is now no condemnation for those who are in Christ Jesus, because through Christ Jesus the law of the Spirit who gives life has set you free from the law of sin and death. For what the law was powerless to do because it was weakened by the flesh, God did by sending his own Son in the likeness of sinful flesh to be a sin offering. And so he condemned sin in the flesh, in order that the righteous requirement of the law might be fully met in us, who do not live according to the flesh but according to the Spirit.

Romans 8:1-4

Read John Stott's inspiring *Bible Speaks Today*[6] series *Message of Romans* commentary on Chapter 8.

Read the biography of Bilquis Sheik *I Dared To Call Him Father*[7] as she recounts her story of turning from Islam to discover the grace of God.

---

6   Stott, J. R. W. (2001). The Message Of Romans: God's Good News For The World, IVP
7   Sheikh, B., (2003) I Dared To Call Him Father, Chosen Books

AIM: To understand how the Spirit of God brings resurrection life that starts now, impacts us on a daily basis and endures forever.

TO SET THE SCENE

Either: How many Zombie movies can the group name in 60 seconds? Why do you think Zombie movies have become so popular?

Or: The critically acclaimed film American Beauty won five Oscars and 89 other awards. The plot revolves around an ordinary middle-aged man called Lester, who is living a very ordinary life, unknowingly with less than a year to live. He opens the film with the words:

"My name is Lester Burnham. This is my neighborhood; this is my street; this is my life. I am 42 years old. In less than a year I will be dead. Of course I don't know that yet, and in a way, I am dead already."

Feelings of insignificance or impotence lead many people to consider their middle-of-the-road life to be a non-life. What are the other symptoms of this malaise in society, or amongst your friends and acquaintances?

 1. During which parts of your day do you feel most like 'the living dead' – that you are merely existing rather than really living? Or think about the times when you feel most alive; why do we not feel like this all the time?

 2. Paul suggests in our next section of Romans 8 that there are two ways to approach life. Christians have the choice to live in reference to their sinful nature or according to the Spirit. He describes one way of life as contributing to a zombie-like existence and the other to celebrating resurrection life. As you read the passage, make a list of the differences between the two types of life.

My thoughts and notes....

READ THE PASSAGE TOGETHER:

⁵Those who live according to the flesh have their minds set on what the flesh desires; but those who live in accordance with the Spirit have their minds set on what the Spirit desires. ⁶The mind governed by the flesh is death, but the mind governed by the Spirit is life and peace. ⁷The mind governed by the flesh is hostile to God; it does not submit to God's law, nor can it do so. ⁸Those who are in the realm of the flesh cannot please God.

⁹You, however, are not in the realm of the flesh but are in the realm of the Spirit, if indeed the Spirit of God lives in you. And if anyone does not have the Spirit of Christ, they do not belong to Christ. ¹⁰But if Christ is in you, then even though your body is subject to death because of sin, the Spirit gives life because of righteousness. ¹¹And if the Spirit of him who raised Jesus from the dead is living in you, he who raised Christ from the dead will also give life to your mortal bodies because of his Spirit who lives in you.

¹²Therefore, brothers and sisters, we have an obligation—but it is not to the flesh, to live according to it. ¹³For if you live according to the flesh, you will die; but if by the Spirit you put to death the misdeeds of the body, you will live.

Romans 8:5-13

3. Paul implies in verse 9 that we are either controlled by the sinful nature or by the Spirit. Does this mean that if we still struggle with sin then the Holy Spirit is not at work in our lives and we are not really Christians? How does the previous chapter on freedom from condemnation help us?

4. Think of some examples or illustrations to describe the conflict many Christians face between the work of the Spirit in our lives and the influence of our sinful nature. When do you feel this conflict most acutely?

John Newton, the hymn writer who penned the famous hymn Amazing Grace once commented with regard to sin in his life:

My thoughts and notes....

*"I am not what I ought to be, I am not what I wish to be, and I am not what I hope to be, but by the grace of God, I am not what I used to be."*⁸

---

8   Paraphrase of quote from John Newton in The Christian Spectator (1821) volume 3, p.186

5. Which of the following statements do you think are true? How do these statements make you feel?

a. Without the Spirit we do not have Christ.

b. Without the Spirit we cannot please God.

c. Without the Spirit we will not be transformed in our affections and behaviours.

d. Without the Spirit we fail to experience life to the full.

 6. Verse 5 says: "Those who live according to the sinful nature have their minds set on what that nature desires; but those who live in accordance with the Spirit have their minds set on what the Spirit desires." Why is our mindset so important? Think of three practical things we could do to make sure that our minds are set on what the Spirit of God desires.

 7. The Christian life is a living paradox, we are both dying and being resurrected. Reflect on the following two quotes – at what times or in which circumstances in your day or week do you feel most drawn to either quote?

Inseparable: Death and Life

In the words of Dr Martin Lloyd Jones:

"The moment we enter into this world and begin to live, we also begin to die. Your first breath is one of the last you will ever take!... the principle of decay, leading to death, is in every one of us."[9]

And the words of the Apostle Paul

"If the Spirit of him who raised Jesus from the dead is living in you, he who raised Christ from the dead will also give life to your mortal bodies because of his Spirit who lives in you"[10]

---

9 Stott, J. R. W. (2001). *The Message Of Romans: God's Good News For The World* (p. 226). Leicester, England; Downers Grove, IL: Inter-Varsity Press.

10 Romans 8:11

8. Because we live in the tension between enjoying the life of the Spirit and living in a decaying body, it is understandable that even for Christians there are times when we feel like spiritual zombies. It is in fact true that we are the living dead. In our worship we need to find a way to connect with both ends of our experience. What are the dangers or opportunities of our worship ending up stuck in a rut of in one of the following extremes?

Worship leader: I know some of you have had a hard week. As we come together to worship today we need to know that no matter how hard it has been, God is with us in our struggle and challenge. We don't need to pretend everything is ok. We need to face the realities of our pain and suffering. God is a suffering God. Christ was nailed to a cross and so there is no pain that we experience that God cannot relate to.

or

Worship leader: I know some of you have had a hard week. As we come together to worship today we need to put all our troubles aside and remember that by the Spirit of God we are connected to the resurrection power of Jesus. There is nothing that is impossible for us because if God can raise Jesus from the dead, then there is no problem in your life that God is not able to overcome.

 9. What do you think it means for you personally to live life to the full? Which area of your life will you pray for the Holy Spirit to bring resurrection power to this week?

REFLECT

You alone can rescue, you alone can save
You alone can lift us from the grave
You came down to find us, led us out of death
To you alone belongs the highest praise[11]

DURING THE WEEK

During Easter we reflect on the inseparable realities of death and life, suffering and celebrating, sacrifice and resurrection. Some fast during Lent, and then feast on Easter Sunday. We meditate on the terrible crucifixion and glorious resurrection of Jesus. We look back and we look forward. We mourn and we rejoice. Perhaps we can try to incorporate these ideas on a smaller scale into our daily routines. Notice things around you that remind you of life and death this week, and deliberately pause to balance your thought life. Balance your prayers between petition and praise. Balance your conversations between talking about your burdens and your blessings.

FOR FURTHER STUDY

Write out the following verses and display them somewhere you'll see them when you are in moments that cause you to feel most zombie-like.

This week try and memorise either Romans 8:10-11, or verses 5-13

But if Christ is in you, then even though your body is subject to death because of sin, the Spirit gives life because of righteousness. And if the Spirit of him who raised Jesus from the dead is living in you, he who raised Christ from the dead will also give life to your mortal bodies because of his Spirit who lives in you.

Romans 8:10-11

Here are two books to help you take this study further.

Peterson, E., (2010) *Practice Resurrection: A Conversation On Growing Up In Christ*, Eerdmans.

NT Wright, (2008) *Surprised By Hope: Rethinking Heaven, The Resurrection, And The Mission Of The Church*, SPCK.

---

11   *"You Alone Can Rescue" Redman, M. & Myrin, J. © 2008 Thankyou Music/Said And Done Music/worshiptogether.com songs/sixsteps Music (Adm. by Integritymusic.com, songs@integritymusic.com)/SHOUT! Music Publishing*

Session 3: "I Feel Worthless"
The Christian Life and the Spirit of Adoption

 AIM: To give people an opportunity to delight in their status as God's adopted children and to work through the implications.

TO SET THE SCENE

Paul has been exploring the difference that living according to the Spirit should make to us. He now comes to a key moment in his argument where he helps us to understand our permanent status in God's family.

Play the Orphan Hero Pictionary game as described in the leaders' notes.

Why do you think the 'orphan hero' is such a frequently appearing theme in western fiction?

Adoption is an often-neglected metaphor of our relationship with God. But rather than contrasting adoption with being an abandoned vulnerable orphan, Paul contrasts it with something else. As we read out this week's passage listen out to what Paul says our adoption is "not" and try and think why he uses this illustration at this point?

READ THE PASSAGE TOGETHER:

> [14]For those who are led by the Spirit of God are the children of God. [15]The Spirit you received does not make you slaves, so that you live in fear again; rather, the Spirit you received brought about your adoption to sonship. And by him we cry, "Abba, Father." [16]The Spirit himself testifies with our spirit that we are God's children. [17]Now if we are children, then we are heirs—heirs of God and co-heirs with Christ, if indeed we share in his sufferings in order that we may also share in his glory.
>
> ***Romans 8:14-17***

 Engaging with the world

1. Read the following account of slavery. What similarities are there between the experience of enslaved people and the spiritual slavery that Paul alludes to in verse 14?

My thoughts and notes....

"Oh! How heavily the weight of slavery pressed upon me then. I must toil day after day, endure abuse and taunts and scoffs, sleep on the hard ground, live on the coarsest fare, and not only this, but live the slave of a blood-seeking wretch, of whom I must stand henceforth in continued fear and dread. Why had I not died in my young years - before God had given me children to love and live for? What unhappiness and suffering and sorrow it would have prevented. I sighed for liberty; but the bondsman's chain was round me, and could not be shaken off. I could only gaze wistfully towards the North, and think of the thousands of miles that stretched between me and the soil of freedom, over which a black freeman may not pass."[12]

Solomon Northup, Twelve Years A Slave

My thoughts and notes....

 2. Why and how does Paul contrast our adoption with slavery? Think about the contrast between how a slave might feel and how an adopted child might feel. Share your own experience of these emotions and feelings.

 3. When we talk about becoming Christians we often use words like, rescued, saved, forgiven, justified and redeemed. Why does "adoption" trump all of those metaphors? What privileges does adoption underline for believers?

 4. Why do you think we don't talk about our adoption into God's family very often? With the notable exception of Ishmael's familiar praise song *Father God, I Wonder*[13] why do you think we rarely sing about being adopted? How do you think we can recover this metaphor in our worship?

 5. According to verses 15 and 16 what is the Holy Spirit's role in our adoption? Note the references to the Trinity. Why is it significant that every member of the Godhead is involved in our story here?

---

12 Northrup, S., (2013) 12 Years A Slave, Penguin
13 "Father God, I Wonder" Smale, I. © 1984 Thankyou Music
     (Adm. by Integritymusic.com, songs@integritymusic.com)

6. "I could never adopt a child – they are usually troubled children who come with emotional baggage, and they would never fit in. They would just be a drain on my time and resources. They are someone else's problem." Imagine if God said that about us! How should our understanding of our spiritual adoption impact the way we respond to children without homes today?

Inseparable: God's adoption of us and our adoption of others

"Does God really want us to be [adoptive] parents? For us it's a no-brainer. Not because we've had a flash of spiritual insight or because we think that adoption is a 'noble cause', but because there's something deeply instinctual and practical about God's desire to put the vulnerable and broken in families. He's done it with us; we want to do it for our children."

Rachel Gardner (Founder of Romance Academy and adoptive mum) [14]

7. Not every Christian is able to adopt or foster a child. But we can all be involved in helping to support those who are demonstrating God's compassion to vulnerable children in our churches. What more could your church be doing to offer ongoing practical support in these areas?

8. Many of us understand what it is like to come from difficult family backgrounds, and for some of us that affects our ability to accept and enjoy being part of God's family. Read verses 16 and 17 again. What signs should we look for in our lives to remind us that we really are fully children of God?

9. How would you respond to somebody who says "I feel worthless"? If anybody is feeling like this in your group today, encourage them by summarising the truths of the passage, and support them through love and prayer.

---

14 *From Home For Good by Krish and Miriam Kandiah, (Hodder) 2013*

REFLECT

Loved with everlasting love,
Led by grace that love to know;
Spirit, breathing from above,
Thou hast taught me it is so.
Oh, this full and perfect peace!
Oh, this transport all divine!
In a love which cannot cease,
I am his, and he is mine.[15]

DURING THE WEEK

Spend some time in prayer thanking God for the privilege of being adopted into his family.

If something has stirred in you about fostering and adoption in the UK, make time to show the Home For Good video in the session, or when you get home. Pray for those families who are fostering or have adopted in your church. Pray for the children in your community who are waiting for adoption.

FOR FURTHER STUDY

Review the memory verses people have been learning.

This week try and memorise either Romans 8:15, or verses 14-17

"The Spirit you received does not make you slaves, so that you live in fear again; rather, the Spirit you received brought about your adoption to sonship. And by him we cry, 'Abba, Father.' The Spirit himself testifies with our spirit that we are God's children."

Romans 8:15

Further helpful reading might include:

Reclaiming Adoption: Missional Living Through The Rediscovery Of Abba Father, edited by Dan Cruver, Cruciform Press (2011)

and

Home For Good: Making A Difference For Vulnerable Children, Krish and Miriam Kandiah, Hodder and Stoughton (2013)

---

15 *"I Am His And He Is Mine" George W. Robinson (1876)*

AIM: To understand how our dissatisfaction can be seen as a godly longing for the restoration of all things and to learn how to channel frustration into change now.

TO SET THE SCENE

What are the things that have caused you the most frustration and angst this week? What was it about them that you found so annoying? Make a list of the top ten things we regularly get frustrated with.

READ THE PASSAGE TOGETHER:

[18]I consider that our present sufferings are not worth comparing with the glory that will be revealed in us. [19]For the creation waits in eager expectation for the children of God to be revealed. [20]For the creation was subjected to frustration, not by its own choice, but by the will of the one who subjected it, in hope [21]that the creation itself will be liberated from its bondage to decay and brought into the freedom and glory of the children of God.

[22]We know that the whole creation has been groaning as in the pains of childbirth right up to the present time. [23]Not only so, but we ourselves, who have the firstfruits of the Spirit, groan inwardly as we wait eagerly for our adoption to sonship, the redemption of our bodies. [24]For in this hope we were saved. But hope that is seen is no hope at all. Who hopes for what they already have? [25]But if we hope for what we do not yet have, we wait for it patiently.

Romans 8:18-25

 1. In verse 18 Paul describes his situation as "present sufferings" that are "not worth comparing with the glory that will be revealed in us." What kinds of suffering were the early Roman Christians and Paul facing? (see 2 Corinthians 11:23-38) How do they compare with our list of top ten frustrations?

My thoughts and notes....

What does the Bible say?

2. How can Paul speak so lightly about his suffering?

What about my church?

3. How do you think Paul would respond to someone who said:

"Jesus initiated the kingdom of God breaking into our world through his earthly ministry. Jesus then won the decisive victory over death, disease and disaster through his death on the cross and resurrection from the dead. So in this life we should experience the victory of God. We should know his power in our bodies through health and in our finances through his blessing. If you have enough faith then your life will be free from suffering."

What does the Bible say?

4. Why should our frustrations not surprise us? What effect did humanity's rebellion against God have on the rest of the world? verses 19-23

Engaging with the world

5. Paul has talked about our frustrations in light of the end of time and in light of the beginning of time. How does placing our frustrations in the centre of this cosmic history help us to understand them?

Engaging with the world

6. Choose one of the following scenarios. How can Paul's verses offer comfort and encouragement? Share your own deep-seated frustrations and how your faith helps you to keep going.

"I have waited five months for an operation that will free my body from pain and still no appointment."

"I struggle every day in a loveless and awkward marriage – I don't know how much longer I can keep going."

"This is the fortieth job application since I was made redundant last year."

> "When pain is to be born, a little courage helps more than much knowledge, a little human sympathy more than much courage, and the least tincture of the love of God more than all."
>
> **C.S. Lewis, *The Problem Of Pain*** [16]

7. In the previous chapter, we looked at how we have been adopted. Here it says we eagerly wait for our adoption. How can we reconcile the fact that it is taught both as a past event and as a future event?

My thoughts and notes....

8. Paul explains the suffering of Christians using the following illustrations:

- Our world is like a hostage waiting for liberation.
- Our world is like a woman in childbirth.
- Christians are like the first fruits of the harvest.

What do these three illustrations have in common? How can we hold together both the pain of our struggles and our hope in the future?

9. It is often said that dissatisfaction is the genesis of innovation. How can we make sure that the dissatisfaction we feel about the world leads us not into resigned apathy but into resolved action? How can we refine our frustrations?

Inseparable: Frustration and Action

Do not even such things as are most bitter to the flesh, tend to awaken Christians to faith and prayer, to a sight of the emptiness of this world, and the fadingness of the best it yield? Doth not God by these things (oft times) call our sins to remembrance, and provoke us to amendment of life? How then can we be offended at things by which we reap so much good?... Therefore if mine enemy hunger, let me feed him; if he thirst, let me give him drink.

John Bunyan, The Entire Works Of John Bunyan: Volume 2 [17]

16   Lewis, C.S. (1941) *The Problem Of Pain*, Centenary Press
17   Bunyan, J., (1860), *The Entire Works Of John Bunyan: Volume 2*, James S Virtue, p.285

REFLECT

There is a hope that lifts my weary head,
A consolation strong against despair,
That when the world has plunged me in its
deepest pit,
I find the Saviour there!
Through present sufferings, future's fear,
He whispers 'courage' in my ear.
For I am safe in everlasting arms,
And they will lead me home.[18]

DURING THE WEEK

As you read the newspaper this week, reflect on the things that frustrate you about the world. Turn your frustrations into prayer about the broken things in the world whether political, environmental, social or personal. Encourage each other to share good news stories of how frustration has encouraged the church to get active in society. You may find inspiration in a publication such as Evangelical Alliance's IDEA magazine which reports stories of churches moved to make a difference both locally and nationally.

FOR FURTHER STUDY

Review the verses we have memorised over the past few weeks, and add the following verse:

This week try and memorise either Romans 8:18, or verses 18-25

"I consider that our present sufferings are not worth comparing with the glory that will be revealed in us."

Romans 8:18

The study of God's future for his universe is called Eschatology. There are helpful sections about this subject in the following books:

Bruce Milne, *Know The Truth* 3rd Edition, IVP, (2009) chapters 27-30

Michael Lloyd, *Café Theology*, Alpha International (2005), p.309-344

---

18 *"There Is A Hope" Stuart Townend & Mark Edwards © 2007 Thankyou Music (Adm. by Integritymusic.com, songs@ integritymusic.com)*

Session 5: "I Feel Weak"
The Christian Life and the Spirit of Prayer

AIM: To explore the role of the Holy Spirit in our prayer lives and discover how God's plans for us give us confidence when we approach God in prayer.

TO SET THE SCENE

Allow a time of quiet prayer to begin.

"The only thing in life that seems to be unchanging, is that life is always changing." Discuss to what extent is this true in our experience, and the connection between our experience, our weaknesses and our prayer life.

> God grant me the serenity to accept the things I cannot change; courage to change the things I can; and wisdom to know the difference.
>
> *Reinhold Niebuhr*

Transition can be a time of great vulnerability. When I was a small boy, my parents once took me in the middle of the night to a beach in Malaysia where we witnessed a giant leatherback turtle, not far off the size of a Volkswagen Beetle, crawl up the sand and bury her eggs. It was an unforgettable experience. We visited a turtle sanctuary the next day and saw footage of the eggs hatching into tiny turtles. Just minutes after they were born they took the most dangerous journey of their lives – from their safe nest under the sand down to the sea. It was during this transition they were most vulnerable. Similarly, as Christians we live in the vulnerable limbo between being born into our new life in Christ and our eternal destiny. In the following verses Paul seeks to comfort disciples caught in the limbo between who we are and who we are going to be.

READ THE PASSAGE TOGETHER:

[26]In the same way, the Spirit helps us in our weakness. We do not know what we ought to pray for, but the Spirit himself intercedes for us through wordless groans. [27]And he who searches our hearts knows the mind of the Spirit, because the Spirit intercedes for God's people in accordance with the will of God.

[28]And we know that in all things God works for the good of those who love him, who have been called according to his purpose. [29]For those God foreknew he also

predestined to be conformed to the image of his Son, that he might be the firstborn among many brothers and sisters. ³⁰And those he predestined, he also called; those he called, he also justified; those he justified, he also glorified.

Romans 8:26-30

 1. Once again the Spirit of God is the focus of this section. Review what we have learned so far about the person and work of the Spirit in our previous four studies in Romans 8. What new aspect of the Spirit's work does Paul pick up on in verses 26-27?

 2. Who should we pray to – God the Father, the Son or the Holy Spirit? Look at verses 27, 34 and 15 to help you.

Inseparable: Trinity and Prayer

There are other prayers in the Bible with different emphases, such as Revelation 22:20 where we call on Jesus to come, or even in the Lord's Prayer where the Spirit is not even mentioned. Although we can pray to Father, the Son or the Holy Spirit directly, by recognising this ancient formula of praying 'to the Father, in the name of the Son, in the power of the Spirit' we can be helped to develop biblical patterns in our prayers. This precept reminds us of the work of Jesus to bring us access to God, the role of the Spirit to empower our prayers and attune our hearts and the sovereignty of God the Father who loves us and whose will we seek.

 3. What do you understand by "groaning" in prayer? What are the three types of groaning Paul describes in the following verses and what is the connection?

- Romans 8:22
- Romans 8:23
- Romans 8:26

 4. In verse 28 Paul writes "And we know that in all things God works for the good of those who love him". In light of the previous question how would you respond to somebody who argued that verse 28 means that life will always be good if we pray?

My thoughts and notes....

5. Romans 8:28 has been both a verse of wonderful comfort and of considerable worry to believers throughout the centuries. What are the challenges it raises? Why do you think this verse has caused such different reactions?

 6. Which of the following do you think are the logical conclusions to draw from Romans 8:28?

- Everything that happens to us occurs because of the direct will of God.
- Everything that happens to us is good.
- Everything that happens to us God can use for our good.

 7. Share some examples from your own life where a difficult situation you encountered, in hindsight, led to something good you could never have expected.

 8. Romans 8:31-39 outlines six parts of every Christian's journey to faith and future hope. Pick one of the words that you find either most encouraging or disturbing and explain why.

 9. How does this list of things God has done for us help us when we feel weak? Share one event happening in the week ahead where you feel particularly vulnerable and pray for one another.

REFLECT

Leader:
Father Almighty, maker of heaven and earth
Set up your kingdom in our midst

Group:
Name places or situations you would like to see
God's rule of peace and justice revealed

Leader:
Lord Jesus Christ, Son of the living God
Have mercy on me, a sinner

Group:
Spend time in silent confession of sins that you
know you need forgiveness for

Leader:
Holy Spirit, breath of the living God
Renew me and all the world

Group:
Name people or situations in need of God's
renewal and healing

Trinitarian prayer adapted from a
prayer written by NT Wright[19]

DURING THE WEEK

Ask for God's help to trust him that he is able to work in every circumstance for our good. Remember the upcoming events that others have shared where they feel vulnerable. On the appropriate day, send them an encouraging note or text. Or pray for them, and ring them afterwards to find out how it went.

---

19   *Bringing The Church To The World, 1992, Bethany House, U.S.A., 209-15*

FOR FURTHER STUDY

This week try and memorise either Romans 8:28, or verses 26-30

And we know that in all things God works for the good of those who love him, who have been called according to his purpose.

Romans 8:28

If you would like to do some further study on prayer look at:

Tom Wright, *New Testament Prayer For Everybody*, SPCK 2012

Pete Greig, *God On Mute: Engaging The Silence Of Unanswered Prayer*, Kingsway, 2007

Alternatively if you wish to delve deeper into the discussion around predestination, then try reading:

McGrath, A. (2010) *Introduction To Christian Theology, Chapter 10 The Doctrine Of Salvation*, p, 315ff
Or
Basinger, D. & Basinger, R. (1986) *Predestination & Free Will: Four Views Of Divine Sovereignty And Human Freedom*, IVP (1986)

Session 6: "I Feel Defeated"
The Christian Life and the Victory of God

 AIM: To strengthen our confidence that God will not let us down, and remind us that we are inseparable from his everlasting love.

TO SET THE SCENE

John is feeling isolated at work. He is the only Christian in his office and finds it hard to fit in with the after-work drinking culture, so doesn't go out with his colleagues. He has tried evangelising his colleagues and even putting little tracts into their Christmas cards, but has rarely had a serious conversation about his faith. John is not finding his work easy and even his boss is asking him to be more productive. John wonders if this is the kind of persecution which is normal for Christians to expect.

If John was in your small group what advice would you give him? In what ways do you feel deflated or defeated when it comes to living out or sharing your faith?

The situation facing the Christians in Rome when Paul wrote his letter is very different to the challenges being faced in the UK today. Just seven years after Paul wrote his letter, a fire broke out and devastated the city. The emperor Nero used Christians as his scapegoat and this led to a time of intense persecution for them. Virtually overnight they became "reputed to be 'enemies of the human race' and credited with such vices as incest and cannibalism. In large numbers, they then became the victims of the imperial malevolence - and it is this persecution of Christians under Nero that traditionally forms the setting for Paul's martyrdom."[20]

We can hardly imagine those dark times where many Christians were tortured viciously including being "burned alive in public."[21] But God knew what was going to happen and sent a message of comfort to those persecuted believers in Rome. As you read it, which parts do you think would have been especially comforting to them?

---

20   Bruce, F. F. (1985). Romans: An Introduction And Commentary (Vol. 6, p. 25). Nottingham, England: Inter-Varsity Press.
21   Judge, 'E. A. (1996). Nero. In (D. R. W. Wood, I. H. Marshall, A. R. Millard, J. I. Packer, & D. J. Wiseman, Eds.) New Bible Dictionary. Leicester, England; Downers Grove, IL: InterVarsity Press.

READ THE PASSAGE TOGETHER:

³¹What, then, shall we say in response to these things? If God is for us, who can be against us? ³²He who did not spare his own Son, but gave him up for us all - how will he not also, along with him, graciously give us all things? ³³Who will bring any charge against those whom God has chosen? It is God who justifies. ³⁴Who then is the one who condemns? No one. Christ Jesus who died - more than that, who was raised to life - is at the right hand of God and is also interceding for us. ³⁵Who shall separate us from the love of Christ? Shall trouble or hardship or persecution or famine or nakedness or danger or sword? ³⁶As it is written:

> "For your sake we face death all day long;
> we are considered as sheep to be slaughtered."

³⁷No, in all these things we are more than conquerors through him who loved us. ³⁸For I am convinced that neither death nor life, neither angels nor demons, neither the present nor the future, nor any powers, ³⁹neither height nor depth, nor anything else in all creation, will be able to separate us from the love of God that is in Christ Jesus our Lord.

Romans 8:31-39

Paul uses five key questions to bring, not just Romans 8 to a dramatic finale, but the whole of his teaching so far in the letter to the Romans. These questions are going to form the basis of our final study as we seek to press these rich truths home to our hearts and minds. Scan through the passage again and identify the five key questions that Paul asks.

1. "What, then, shall we say in response to these things?"

My thoughts and notes....

Spend some time reviewing the key things we have learned in Romans 8 so far. What shall we say to God in response to all of this truth? Allow your eyes to scan back over the last five sessions and find a specific promise or teaching or challenge and write a one-line prayer to God in response.

2. If God is for us who can be against us? What kind of confidence does Paul want us to have in verse 31?

3. Verse 31 has sometimes been misquoted in an attempt to justify Christians taking others to court, or a country going to war, or a church applying for planning permission for an extension. How do we work out whether God really is "for us" in an undertaking?

 4. Verse 31 offers us great confidence when we are feeling defeated. This can lead to a confidence in prayer when we approach God. What is the logic of verse 32 when it comes to prayer? Think of an illustration that may help a young believer develop greater confidence in prayer.

Listen, my friend! Your helplessness is your best prayer. It calls from your heart to the heart of God with greater effect than all your uttered pleas. He hears it from the very moment that you are seized with helplessness, and He becomes actively engaged at once in hearing and answering the prayer of your helplessness.

O Hallesby Prayer [22]

 5. The two questions contained in verses 32 and 34 focus in on our standing before God. From what you know about the book of Romans what would Paul say was the reason that no one can bring any charge against us and no one can condemn us? How does this reason help us in times of difficulty?

6. Generations of Christians have found great comfort in the answer to the question: "Who shall separate us from the love of Christ?" In verse 35 Paul lists seven things that might threaten to separate us from Christ. Identify them and add to them the things that believers you know struggle with at the moment.

 7. Paul assures us that nothing can separate from Christ's love in verse 35, reiterated again in verse 37 where we are

---

22 Hallesby, O. (1994) Prayer, Augsburg books ,p.19

described as more than conquerors. However in between these two verses he quotes from Psalm 44, implying that persecution is normal. How do you reconcile these two points? (see also 2 Timothy 3:12)

Inseparable: Victors and Victims

"We are conquerors: though killed all the day long, yet conquerors. A strange way of conquering, but it was Christ's way; thus he triumphed over principalities and powers in his cross. It is a surer and a nobler way of conquest by faith and patience than by fire and sword."

Matthew Henry, An Exposition Of The Old And New Testament, Volume 6[23]

 8. In verses 38-39 Paul paints a comprehensive picture of the challenges that face a Christian. Which of these areas do you struggle with most? Why does being connected to Christ by faith mean that none of the following things will ultimately defeat us?

▶ Death nor life?
Romans 6:5, John 11:21-25

▶ Angels nor demons?
Ephesians 6:12, Philippians 2:5-11

▶ Present nor future nor any powers?
Romans 8:18, Hebrews 13:8

▶ Height nor depth nor anything else in all creation? *Colossians 1:15-18*

What about my church? **9.** Twice in this passage, Paul drives home that we are inseparable from the love of Christ (verse 35 and 39). Sometimes our biggest problem is thinking that we can separate ourselves from Christ's love – because of our sin, our lack of worship, our busyness. How can we encourage one another to take hold of God's promise that nothing can separate us?

---

23 Henry, M., (1838) An Exposition Of The Old And New Testament, Volume 6, Haswell, Barrington, and Haswell, p. 337

REFLECT

Keep me safe, my God, for in you I take refuge.

I say to the Lord, "You are my Lord; apart from you I have no good thing."

I say of the holy people who are in the land, "They are the noble ones in whom is all my delight."

Those who run after other gods will suffer more and more. I will not pour out libations of blood to such gods or take up their names on my lips.

Lord, you alone are my portion and my cup; you make my lot secure.

The boundary lines have fallen for me in pleasant places; surely I have a delightful inheritance.

I will praise the Lord, who counsels me; even at night my heart instructs me.

I keep my eyes always on the Lord. With him at my right hand, I will not be shaken.

Therefore my heart is glad and my tongue rejoices; my body also will rest secure,

because you will not abandon me to the realm of the dead, nor will you let your faithful one see decay.

You make known to me the path of life; you will fill me with joy in your presence, with eternal pleasures at your right hand.

Psalm 16:4-11

DURING THE WEEK

In the fifth century, reading the book of Romans helped Augustine come to faith. This faith led him into a life of seeking to spread and defend the gospel through his preaching and writing. These writings have shaped not just the church, but much of western philosophy and culture. In the twentieth century, reading the book of Romans prompted in Karl Barth a revitalised faith that led to him becoming the theological driving force behind the confessing church, which in turn challenged the right of the Nazi government to dictate how the church should live. Resistance and renewal were two results that the book of Romans brought in the lives, not just of these two men, but countless women and men across the world and through the ages. Our prayer, as you come to the end of these studies, is that you would know the work of the Spirit in your life to assure you that if you are a believer you have nothing to fear from God who declares that there is "No condemnation for those who are in Christ Jesus" (Romans 8:1), and that there is nothing to fear on earth because "nothing can separate us from the love of God that is ours in Christ Jesus" (Romans 8:39). Resolve to come back to this chapter regularly – maybe once a week or once a month so you don't forget these truths and they become rooted in your own life and faith.

FOR FURTHER STUDY

Review the verses we have memorised over the past few weeks, and add the following verse Romans 8: 37-39:

In all these things we are more than conquerors through him who loved us. For I am convinced that neither death nor life, neither angels nor demons, neither the present nor the future, nor any powers, neither height nor depth, nor anything else in all creation, will be able to separate us from the love of God that is in Christ Jesus our Lord.

Romans 8:37-39

NT Wright's short book Evil And The Justice Of God offers a concise and comprehensive introduction to the effects of evil in the world and how Christ has ultimately defeated evil through the cross. On a similar vein John Stott's classic The Cross Of Christ has a very helpful chapter called 'The Conquest Of Evil' which offers an inspirational picture of how Jesus has undone the powers of sin and corruption through his atoning death.

Leaders' Guide

TO HELP YOU LEAD

You may have led a group many times before or this may be your first time. Here is some advice on how to lead these studies.

- As a group leader, you don't have to be an expert or a lecturer. You are there to facilitate the learning of the group members – helping them to discover for themselves the wisdom in God's word. You should not be doing most of the talking or dishing out the answers, whatever the group expects from you!

- You do need to be aware of the group's dynamics, however. People can be quite quick to label themselves and each other in a group situation. One person might be seen as the expect, another the moaner who always has something to complain about. One person may be labelled as quiet and not expected to contribute; another person may always jump in with something to say. Be aware of the different type of individuals in the group, but don't allow the labels to stick. You may need to encourage those who find it hard to get a word in, and quieten down those who always have something to say. Talk to members between sessions to find out how they feel about the group.

- The sessions are planned to try and engage every member in active learning. Of course you cannot force anyone to take part if they don't want to, but it won't be too easy to be a spectator. Activities that ask everyone to write down a word, or talk in twos, and then report back to the group are there for a reason. They give everyone space to think and form their opinion, even if not everyone voices it out loud.

- Do adapt the sessions for your group as you feel is appropriate. Some groups may know each other very well and will be prepared to talk at a deep level. New groups may take a bit of time to get to know each other before making themselves vulnerable, but encourage members to share their lives with each other.

- You probably won't be able to tackle all the questions in each session so decide in advance which ones are most appropriate to your group and situation.

Session 6: "I Feel Defeated" 39

- Encourage a number of replies to each question. The study is not about finding a single right answer, but about sharing experiences and thoughts in order to find out how to apply the Bible to people's lives. When brainstorming, don't be too quick to evaluate the contributions. Write everything down and then have a look to see which suggestions are worth keeping.

- Similarly, encourage everyone to ask questions, voice doubts and discuss difficulties. Some parts of the Bible are difficult to understand. Sometimes the Christian faith throws up paradoxes. Painful things happen to us that make it difficult to see what God is doing. A group should be a safe place to express all of this. If discussion doesn't resolve the issue, send everyone away to pray about it between sessions, and ask your minister for advice.

- Give yourself time in the week to read through the Bible passage and the questions. Read the Leaders' notes for the session, as different ways of presenting the questions are sometimes suggested. However during the session don't be too quick to come in with the answer – sometimes people need space to think.

- Delegate as much as you like! The easiest activities to delegate are reading the text, and the worship sessions, but there are other ways to involve the group members. Giving people responsibility can help them own the session much more.

- Pray for group members by name, that God would meet with them during the week. Pray for the group session, for a constructive and helpful time. Ask the Lord to equip you as you lead the group.

THE STRUCTURE OF EACH SESSION

Feedback: find out what people remember from the previous session, or if they have been able to act during the week on what was discussed last time.

To set the scene: an activity or question to get everyone thinking about the subject to be studied.

Bible reading: it's important actually to read the passage you are studying during the session. Ask someone to prepare this in advance or go around the group reading a verse or two each. Don't assume everyone will be happy to read out loud.

Questions and activities: adapt these as appropriate to your group. Some groups may enjoy a more activity-based approach; some may prefer just to discuss the questions. Try out some new things!

Worship: suggestions for creative worship and prayer are included, which give everyone an opportunity to respond to God, largely individually. Use these alongside singing or other group expressions of worship. Add a prayer time with opportunities to pray for group members and their families and friends.

For next week: this gives a specific task to do during the week, helping people to continue to think about or apply what they have learned.

Further study: suggestions are given for those people who want to study the themes further. These could be included in the group if you feel it's appropriate and if there is time.

WHAT YOU NEED

A list of materials that are needed is printed at the start of each session in the Leaders' Guide. In addition you will probably need:

Bibles: the main Bible passage is printed in the book so that all the members can work from the same version. It is useful to have other Bibles available, or to ask everyone to bring their own, so that other passages can be referred to.

Paper and pens: for people who need more space than is in the book!

Flip chart: it is helpful to write down people's comments during a brainstorming session, so that none of the suggestions is lost. There may not be space for a proper flip chart in the average lounge, and having one may make it feel too much like a business meeting or lecture. Try getting someone to write on a big sheet of paper on the floor or coffee table, and then stick this up on the wall with blu-tack.

GROUND RULES

How do people know what is expected of them in a group situation? Is it ever discussed, or do we just pick up clues from each other? You may find it helpful to discuss some ground rules for the group at the start of this course, even if your group has been going a long time. This also gives you an opportunity to talk about how you, as the leader, see the group. Ask everyone to think about what they want to get out of the course. How do they want the group to work? What values do they want to be part of the group's experience; honesty, respect, confidentiality? How do they want their contributions to be treated? You could ask everyone to write down three ground rules on slips of paper and put them in a bowl. Pass the bowl around the group. Each person takes out a rule and reads it, and someone collates the list. Discuss the ground rules that have been suggested and come up with a top five. This method enables everyone to contribute fairly anonymously. Alternatively, if your group are all quite vocal, have a straight discussion about it!

NB Not all questions in each session are covered, some are self-explanatory.

ICONS

 The aim of the session

 Investigate what else the Bible says

 How does this apply to me?

 What about my church?

 Engaging with the world

Session 1: Notes - "I Feel Guilty"
The Christian Life and the Spirit of Freedom

YOU WILL NEED

- You could photocopy Jenny's dilemma from the introduction so each pair has a copy of it to read through for the set the scene segment.

- It's helpful for each member of the group to have a Bible as well as a workbook.

- If you decide to take up the memorisation challenge for Romans chapter 8 prepare some cards for each of your house group members to make it easier for them to remember the passage or verse they are going to try and learn.

- You will also need some paper and drawing equipment for the worship response (see below).

TO SET THE SCENE

We need to make sure that as a church we don't try and send everyone home on a guilt trip at the end of the service. The gospel is good news that we have been forgiven by God not because of the good things we have done, but because of the good that Jesus has done on our behalf. As we explore the passage, let's pray we are left with a deeper conviction of the liberating news of the gospel.

DISCUSS TOGETHER

1. God is not going to condemn us due to our sins past, present or future. This promise is only available to those who are "in Christ Jesus". This surely means that if we are not in Christ Jesus, we still stand condemned in front of holy God because of our sin.

2. Being united with Christ means all of the riches that are connected with Christ become connected with us. As 2 Corinthians 8:9 puts it: "For you know the grace of our Lord Jesus Christ, that though he was rich, yet for your sake he became poor, so that you through his poverty might become rich."

Romans 6:11 Because we are inseparable from Christ through faith our sin is no longer counted against us (we are dead to our sins) but we are given new life through our faith in Jesus.

Romans 6:23 Because we are inseparable from Christ through faith we no longer are under the death penalty that our sins deserve but now we have received the gift of life instead.

Romans 8:39 We are inseparably connected to the love of God by being united to Jesus by faith. We will come back to this verse later on in our study series, but for now it is enough to recognize the link – being in Christ means that we are inseparable from him. This is comforting and liberating.

3. All of these illustrations are valid ways of understanding what it means for us to live "in Christ". Some will be more meaningful than others, depending on our interests and experiences.

4. Verse 2 – The Spirit brings freedom, whereas the law brings subjection.

Verse 3 – The Spirit has power where the law was powerless.

Verse 4 – The Spirit brings salvation, uniting us to Jesus' work on the cross, while the law set standards that nobody could achieve and therefore brought condemnation.

5. According to Romans 8:5-7, in order for anyone to be able to live to please God they must have the Spirit at work in them. Only those who have received the Spirit have been set free from the law of death and sin. So the Spirit must be at work in us for us to become Christians at all. Indeed the Spirit makes us children of God – see 8:14-15.

6. Jesus lived a life that perfectly measured up to the requirements of the law. When Jesus died he was an innocent victim willingly taking upon himself the full punishment for all of us who are lawbreakers so that we could be redeemed; that is, set free from the law's hold over us. Through the Spirit's work we are connected to Christ, and also now that the Holy Spirit lives in us we choose to live in a way that honours Jesus. See Romans 6:1-4 for more on this. This means that even though day by day we all struggle to live up to God's perfect standards, through Christ's work on our behalf we stand before God blameless. When I fail, I know that Christ's life of good works and death for my sin guarantee me a right standing before God.

7. Through the grace of God we are forgiven for all of our sins. My value and worth in front of God is independent of the amount of good works we show now. It is independent of what we have done in the past - even sins that I am currently committing. That said, if the Spirit of God is at work in our lives he will convict us of areas of our lives that are in need of his transformation, so that we more resemble Christ in all aspects including our hospitality, the impact we have on others and our sexual purity. Being inseparable from Christ must mean that we no longer enjoy living in a way that is opposed to the way he lived.

8. If God does not condemn us because of our sin any more then we cannot use condemnation and guilt as a means of control in our churches. We can, however, call people to cooperate with the Spirit's work in their lives, to say no to our old fleshly way of living and to say yes to the things that will please the Spirit. There is a difference between guilt and conviction. If we are not careful, guilt can be a means of manipulation where we attempt to convince someone that their standing before God is somehow based on their works, performance or our goodness. Conviction can mean that we recognise that a way of living is no longer appropriate for someone who has been forgiven and restored to relationship with a Holy God.

9. Instead of playing on someone's insecurities in persuasion we need to help someone understand their new identity in Christ.

When trying to recruit someone for a task in the church:

Try and help people see how the role will help them grow in their relationship with God.

Try and help people see how the role will help them to serve God's purposes.

Try and match a person's gifts and experience with a need or opportunity.

Try and help people experience a range of different roles until they can find one that suits them.

Be careful how long someone ends up doing a job – try and not make it a lifetime commitment with no end in sight.

Keep in mind we are less interested in getting people to do jobs but rather to grow people through jobs.

Help people understand that serving on rotas is a valid and valuable means of personal worship of a God who also works hard to serve our needs.

Give people a sense of vision for why the role is really important to what God is doing in the church.

WORSHIP

Hand out paper and pens and encourage people to write a prayer, sketch a picture or copy out the verse from Romans 8:1-4 that most inspired them this study. You could play some music in the background while people are writing. For example, *No Condemnation* by Brian Doerkson or *And Can It Be* by Charles Wesley. Once the time is over, ask people if they are willing to show the rest of the group what they have written or drawn and explain why.

Session 2: Notes - "I Feel Dead"
The Christian Life and the Spirit of Resurrection

YOU WILL NEED

▶ If it is appropriate for your group to be shown a film rated 15, you could show the opening sequence of American Beauty starting with the American Beauty film title and the narrative "My name is Lester Burnham" - end with the words "dead already" at 1 min 50 seconds.

▶ Memory verse card with

"But if Christ is in you, then even though your body is subject to death because of sin, the Spirit gives life because of righteousness. And if the Spirit of him who raised Jesus from the dead is living in you, he who raised Christ from the dead will also give life to your mortal bodies because of his Spirit who lives in you."

Romans 8:11-13

TO SET THE SCENE

If you are not using the American Beauty movie, you could play a game to see how many Zombie movies the group or subgroups can guess in 60 seconds. Here are 12 to help you get started:

1. Night Of The Living Dead
2. Shaun Of The Dead
3. 28 Days
4. Zombieland
5. Resident Evil
6. World War Z
7. Warm Bodies
8. Day Of The Dead
9. Evil Dead
10. I Was A Teenage Zombie
11. Paranorman
12. Pet Cemetery

This may result in a debate as to whether it is helpful or not for Christians to watch these types of films. Zombie movies are certainly not for everyone but it is important to understand the culture in which we live. Perhaps those who have watched some of these films can talk about how it helps them understand the culture around us, and how it helps them understand their faith better.

DISCUSS TOGETHER

1. Many people feel like a cog in a giant wheel in their work place. Some people feel that their daily commute is mind-numbingly boring. Others feel the daily grind when getting children ready for school or caring for elderly relatives. Be aware that some people may feel that everything about their lives is tedious and difficult, whereas others may feel that life is always fun. Help group members understand one another by being open about their attitude to life, where it comes from and how they might want it to change in the future.

2. Paul contrasts life in the Spirit with life in the flesh

▶ Verse 5: What is your mind set on – do you think about God or physical appetites?

▶ Verse 6: Does your thought life revolve around life and peace or death and conflict?

▶ Verse 7-8: Is your attitude hostile to God or wanting to please God?

▶ Verse 9: Do you belong to Jesus, or belong to the world?

▶ Verse 10: Are you concerned more about your physical decline, or your spiritual growth and resurrection life?

▶ Verse 12: Do you want to kill sin and live, or live in sin and die?

3. If there is no difference in our lives and attitude to sin since before we were Christians, then we should be worried that the Spirit is not in us and ask if we really are Christians at all. Spirit-filled Christians will struggle with sin – as verses 12-13 confirm. We will live in a constant battle to rid ourselves of it. However if we fight sin and temptation, rather than unquestioningly ignore it or give in to it, then this is a sign that we are filled with the Spirit. For those falling in the second category, we can claim the promise that if we are in Christ there is no condemnation.

4. Poison in a snake is natural, and so causes the snake little trouble, while that same poison in a human body causes all sorts of trouble. Similarly before we were Christians, sin was a normal part of our lives. However when we become Christians, that same sin in our life is unnatural and toxic to our relationship with God, so we feel troubled about it.[24]

5. ▶ Without the Spirit we do not have Christ – true verse 9

▶ Without the Spirit we cannot please God – true verse 8

▶ Without the Spirit we will not be transformed – true verse 5-7

▶ Without the Spirit we do not know life to the full – true verse 11

---

24 *Paraphrase of Thomas Waton: There is as much difference between sin in the wicked and sin in the godly—as between poison being in a serpent and poison being in a man. Poison in a serpent is in its natural place and is delightful—but poison in a man's body is harmful and he uses antidotes to expel it. So sin in a wicked man is delightful, being in its natural place—but sin in a child of God is burdensome and he uses all means to expel it. Thomas Watson's "The Godly Man's Picture" (1620-1680)*

6. Here are two ways to encourage your group.

Agree with your home group to set a daily alarm together for a certain time of the day. When this alarm goes off you could silently pray the Lord's prayer or pray for another member of your group.

Find ways to integrate scripture into the routine of your daily life. For example invest in some Bible teaching recordings to listen to on your commute, or copy out some of Romans 8 onto cards and leave them in strategic places in your home to remind you to live according to the Spirit.

7. Our lives are an inseparable combination of death and life, as it states in Romans 8:10. We experience both our aging and decaying bodies and the renewal of the Spirit. While we wait for our full redemption we experience both the sorrows and struggles of life on earth and miraculous tasters of the life to come. We experience great beauty and brokenness in our world. This combination is part of the normal Christian life.

8. The Bible has space for both laughter and lament in our worship, both woe and wonder, celebration and consolation. If our worship is biblical we must allow the full range of emotions to be a part of our corporate worship.[25]

9. Every area of our life needs to experience the resurrection power of God. God is interested not just in the time we spend in quiet with him, church service or family but every moment of every day. Help your group explore areas that might need more attention? For example, what do you think experiencing Christ's resurrection power in your commute to work, or your visit to a sick neighbour would look like?

WORSHIP

Divide into pairs and encourage everyone to share one time in their week when they feel like a spiritual zombie. Why not set an alarm on your phone or watch to remember to pray for your partner at that exact moment in the coming week.

Songs that may help group members respond to this include:

Knowing You, Jesus by Graham Kendrick
You Alone Can Rescue by Matt Redman & Jonas Myrin

---

25   see Krish Kandiah, *Route 66: A Crash Course In Navigating Life With The Bible*, Monarch 2011.

Session 3: Notes - "I Feel Worthless"
The Christian Life and the Spirit of Adoption

YOU WILL NEED

- Pieces of paper and pens for the teams to be able to write their list of orphans in film and literature for the Orphan Hero Pictionary game to set the scene.

- Download the *Home For Good* video from:
  http://www.homeforgood.org.uk/home-for-good-a-short-promotional-film/

- Find out how many families in your church are fostering and adopting. If you can find out any prayer needs they might have that would be really helpful for the prayer and worship time this week.

- Memory Verse cards with the following Bible text:
  "The Spirit you received does not make you slaves, so that you live in fear again; rather, the Spirit you received brought about your adoption to sonship.And by him we cry, 'Abba, Father.' The Spirit himself testifies with our spirit that we are God's children."

  Romans 8:15-17

TO SET THE SCENE

"Orphan Hero Pictionary". Divide into two teams and play group Pictionary.

Ask for the most artistic member of each team to come out to the front to receive a list of orphans in literature; without saying anything they need to draw a picture to help the rest of their team guess the orphan. There are no words or miming allowed in the drawing. Once a person on their team correctly guesses the orphan the artist moves on to the next person and so on until the last orphan is guessed. The team that finishes the list first is the winner.

1. Batman
2. Anne Of Green Gables
3. James Bond
4. Superman
5. Moses
6. Harry Potter
7. Luke Skywalker
8. Frodo Baggins
9. Spiderman
10. The 3 Girls from Despicable Me

DISCUSS TOGETHER

1. The quote used in the session is taken from the book that is now an award-winning film. Just like physical slaves, spiritual slaves have:

  a. Lost their freedom – spiritual slavery means we are not free to do what we want to do (see Romans 7)

  b. Live in fear – spiritual slavery means we are held captive through fear (see Hebrews 2:15)

  c. Are only kept as long as they are useful – spiritual slavery means you are expendable and you have no right to a place in the family (see John 8:33-36)

2. Paul contrasts our adoption with slavery in Romans 8 by drawing attention to the fact that once we are adopted we no longer live under fear. We are now made eternal children of our heavenly father, and co-heirs with Christ. Encourage people to talk openly if they feel like a 'slave' to their housework, their paid work, demanding family members etc. Similarly, encourage people to talk openly about how their Christian faith makes a difference in these areas.

3. Being justified means that our legal and moral record in front of God is wiped clean.

Being forgiven means that God no longer counts my sin against me anymore.

Being redeemed means that God has paid the price to release me from slavery.

Being rescued means that God has taken me out of the situation that threatened my life and eternal life.

But they all describe something that has happened in the past. At the end of all these truths I could still be alone, back where I started, without hope. Adoption means that I am intimately connected to my heavenly Father and my brother Jesus Christ. I have a legal status as a member of God's family. I have a home and a hope and an inheritance. I have somewhere I belong that can never be taken away. Remind everyone of the title of this book - Inseparable - and apply it to a family bond.

4. Is it possible we don't often encounter the use of the metaphor of adoption because:

It is too passive as a metaphor – we don't do anything to get adopted and we like to think that we play a part in our salvation?

It is too familiar we would rather have a legal relationship with God than an intimate familial one?

It is a taboo in our society. Traditionally we have kept adoptions secret as in the past it has often been associated with illegitimate children, underage parents or worse?

Adoption reminds us of the plight of vulnerable children in our society and our responsibility to them, so it is safer to avoid the metaphor?

5. The Holy Spirit is the member of the Trinity through whom we received adoption (verse 15). The Spirit gives us the confidence to call God Abba Father (verse 15). The Spirit is the one who bears testimony in our hearts that we are truly God's children (verse 16) and gives us the hope that comes from being co-heirs with Christ.

6. Many people hesitate to think about adoption because they are nervous about taking on "difficult" children. When God adopted us he knew he was getting "troubled" children who needed to be rescued from slavery to sin and emotional and spiritual trauma. Adoption is not only a practical human need close to God's heart (James 1:27, Psalm 68:5-6, Isaiah 1:17), it is also a powerful parable or visual aid of the grace of God.

7. Some churches have offered the use of their buildings to social services for supervised contact meetings between children in care and their birth parents. Church buildings are often a lot nicer and more humane than council facilities and it helps to break down barriers between social services and churches. Some foster or adoptive parents find the 24/7 care they offer to vulnerable children exhausting. Can your church encourage members to help with regular baby sitting or DIY or other practical support such as providing meals or lifts to offer the family regular relief and support?

8. Some people who have experienced difficult home backgrounds find it easier to enjoy being part of God's family because they appreciate it so much more. Others come with the inbuilt expectation that they will be let down or betrayed. For those of us who doubt our full and loving acceptance as children of God, there are three possible signals to help us. Firstly we should look for some spiritual awareness or conviction. This feeling is rarely a permanent feature of our Christian life, or Paul would not have had to mention it. But occasionally we may feel drawn to our Father God in a special way. Secondly there is a future reality – something to look forward to – an expectation, of sharing in God's eternity. Thirdly there is likely to be suffering, not pointless suffering, but suffering that draws us closer to

Jesus, and brings us towards his glory.

9. Be aware that feelings of worthlessness may be symptomatic of depression, and anybody expressing this may need professional medical or counselling help.

WORSHIP

Hand out some small pieces of paper and ask people to write and then fill in "You are valuable because……" Fold the papers up, write the name of another group member on the top and then place in a pile on the table. The papers can then be distributed to help combat feelings of worthlessness.

Why not sing together, or play in the background the hymn:

Loved With Everlasting Love by George Wade Robinson & Robert J Hughes

You could also Show the Home For Good video and share prayer information from the fostering and adopting families in your church.

http://www.eauk.org/church/campaigns/home-for-good/

Session 4: Notes - "I Feel Frustrated"
The Christian Life and the Spirit of Restoration

YOU WILL NEED

- The top 10 headlines from the week's newspapers.

- Memory Verse cards with the following Bible text:

  "I consider that our present sufferings are not worth comparing with the glory that will be revealed in us. "

  Romans 8:18

TO SET THE SCENE

Ask people to share the things that have been annoying them this week. This is often the first thing that some people share when they are arriving or having coffee together. So feel free to remind people of what they have already disclosed earlier in the evening. Here are the top ten annoying things from a survey done by a British Building Society.[26] Why do you think we get so frustrated by seemingly small things?

1. Pressure selling
2. Spam emails
3. Pushy sales people
4. Foreign call centres
5. Being put on hold
6. Dog mess on the pavement
7. Pot holes in the road
8. Spam text messages
9. Drivers who take up two parking spaces
10. Getting stuck behind really slow drivers

DISCUSS TOGETHER

1. In 2 Corinthians 11:23-38 Paul outlines some of the struggles he was facing as a Christian. He similarly describes them as "light and momentary" (2 Corinthinas 4:17) These help set the context when we speak about facing struggles in our context. Paul's battles include imprisonment, physical torture and violence, forced relocation, persecution, hunger and thirst, stress at church, and personal spiritual struggles.

2. Paul in no way minimises the reality or pain of the suffering he and the Christians of his day were facing, but he holds them in comparison with the hope of the glory he was looking forward to. Paul seems to have such a clear vision for and confidence in God's ultimate victory and vindication that his own suffering seems light and momentary in comparison.

26 http://www.news.com.au/lifestyle/the-50-most-annoying-things-in-life/story-fneszs56-1226675916755

3. I imagine Paul would be pretty direct and refute this approach to suffering. The New Testament never promises complete victory for the believer this side of the fulfilment of the ages. Here Paul is writing about waiting patiently for what is to come, not experiencing it in the present. As we saw in the last session, suffering and trouble is promised for God's people by both Jesus (John 16:33) and Paul (2 Timothy 3:12).

4. Paul describes in this chapter the fact that the fall of humanity had a knock-on effect on the whole of creation. He describes how the whole of creation is subject to frustration (verses 19-21). Here Paul is simply explaining the consequences of the fall of humanity recorded in Genesis 3. There we see how sin affected human relationship with God (Genesis 3:8); human relationships with each other (Genesis 3:7); human relationships with the creation (Genesis 3:17) and human relationships with ourselves (Genesis 3:19).[27]

5. Some Christians live as if the physical world is of no value and that environmental concern is a liberal accommodation to prevailing cultural trends. Romans 8 describes God's vision for creation being liberated from its bondage (Romans 8:21). Everything will be renewed and restored not just human beings escaping with their souls from a dying planet.

6. When God adopted us it was not because of anything we had done, it was in spite of the sin and brokenness we brought with us. God's compassion should set the benchmark for our own.

7. Bring out the top ten news stories that you have gathered from this week's news. Ask people to rate which of the news stories makes them the most frustrated. Spend a few moments in prayer asking that the dissatisfaction and frustration we feel with the world would lead us into deeper engagement with the world, rather than apathy.

8. The Spirit prompts hope in us. Hope is a rare commodity in our society - our film industry shows us very few positive depictions about the future. The Spirit prompts patience in us that we can trust God that his future plans will come to fruition. The Spirit prompts action in us (the book of Acts demonstrates the Spirit to be the missionary force behind the church's explosion across the world, bringing good news wherever it went).

---

27   Kandiah, K.(2007) Destiny, Monarch

9. We may be very good at being frustrated with potholes in the road and call centres, but very bad at being frustrated with the injustice in the world, or the lack of compassion for those in poverty. By spending more time in God's word, and in prayer and worship we can refine our frustrations to bring them in line with his heart.

WORSHIP

Take a look at the top ten news stories this week. Which prompt us to want to take action and what can we actually do? Share ideas big and small that can channel our frustration into action.

Songs that may help group members respond to this include:

For This I Have Jesus by Graham Kendrick

There Is A Hope by Stuart Townend & Mark Edwards

Session 5: Notes - "I Feel Weak"
The Christian Life and the Spirit of Prayer

YOU WILL NEED

- Print out a few copies of the Trinitarian Liturgy we will use in this session if members do not have study guides.

  Leader:
  Father almighty, maker of heaven and earth
  Set up your kingdom in our midst

  Group:
  Name places or situations you would like to see God's rule of peace and justice revealed

  Leader:
  Lord Jesus Christ, Son of the living God
  Have mercy on me, a sinner

  Group:
  Spend time in silent confession of sins that you know you need forgiveness for

  Leader:
  Holy Spirit, breath of the living God
  Renew me and all the world

  Group:
  Name people or situations in need of God's renewal and healing

- Memory verse card with

  "And we know that in all things God works for the good of those who love him, who have been called according to his purpose. For those God foreknew he also predestined to be conformed to the image of his Son, that he might be the firstborn among many brothers and sisters. And those he predestined, he also called; those he called, he also justified; those he justified, he also glorified."

  Romans 8:28-30

TO SET THE SCENE

Tell the group we will open in prayer. Without warning, spend three minutes in silence. What happens next? Ask people how they felt, what came into their minds, whether those three minutes were helpful spiritually. What problems did they have praying?

DISCUSS TOGETHER

1. So far in our study of Romans chapter 8 we have learned that:

▶ Verse 2 The Spirit gives life

▶ Verse 4 The Spirit unites us with Christ so that righteous requirements of the law are met in us

▶ Verse 5 The Spirit inspires us to set our minds on the things of the Spirit

▶ Verse 6 The mind governed by the Spirit has life and peace

▶ Verse 9 The Spirit unites us with Christ and without the Spirit we cannot know Christ

▶ Verse 10 The Spirit unites us with the power of Christ's resurrection

▶ Verse 13 The Spirit empowers us to put to death our wrongdoing

▶ Verse 14 Through the Spirit we receive adoption into God's family

▶ Verse 15 By the Spirit we have confidence to call God Abba Father

▶ Verse 16 The Spirit reassures us that we are God's children

▶ Verse 22 The Spirit troubles us as we long for the fulfilment of our adoption

Now we are going to consider the Spirit's work in our prayer life

2. In Romans 8, Paul shows how the members of the Trinity are involved in our prayers. Verse 27 shows us that the Spirit helps us because he knows both our hearts and God's purposes. From this unique place he is able to speak on our behalf to God even when we run out of words. Verse 34 shows that Jesus is also interceding on our behalf but the emphasis here is on Jesus pleading our case that we might receive the forgiveness of sins. Verse 15 reminds us that our prayers are directed to God our Father, in the context of our relationship with him.

3. The three types of groaning described in Romans

    a. Creation groaning as it waits for its restoration (Romans 8:22)

    b. Christians groaning as we await the completion of our adoption into God's family and the full restoration of our bodies (Romans 8:23)

   c. The Spirit groaning for us when we don't know what words to speak in prayer (Romans 8:26)

They all describe a communication born of frustration. Sometimes it may feel that we are the only one struggling, but Paul wants us to know that the whole world and even God himself longs for the completion of our salvation. We are to bring our weaknesses and struggles to God, even if we don't know how to express them in words.

Scholars are divided in their opinions on how to interpret verse 26. It could mean that:

   a. The Spirit of God can help us pray when we don't know what to pray

   b. The Spirit of God prays on our behalf when we can't find the words

   c. The Spirit of God empowers our prayers

Encourage your group to pick the answer they think expresses the sense of the passage and their experience and encourage them to make a good case for what they believe.

4. Many Christians claim that we should live in unending glory and victory. However Paul makes it very clear that although God is working everything out ultimately for his good purpose and final restoration, we live in the transition time where we experience weakness, struggles and frustration.

5. We draw comfort from the fact that we cannot see the whole picture. Just like a beautiful tapestry cannot be made without sharp needles and chopped threads, so we trust that our current problems are under God's control. However this verse is also controversial – does the "all things" include our sin, the terrible atrocities of evil dictators, or the catastrophic effects of natural disasters?

6. This is very difficult ground to cover concisely. Scholars have been wrestling with these concepts for 2000 years.

   If everything that happens to us does so because of the direct will of God, there would be little place for free will or for human moral responsibility. The Bible teaches that God is the rightful ruler of the whole universe but that somehow God's rule is not fully realised on earth, and that our free will is real. Hence we pray that God's kingdom will one day come on earth as it is in heaven in the Lord's prayer – the implication being that there is more to come of God's rule on earth, and that we have a part to play.

The Bible is clear that many bad things happen, even to Christians. For example Paul himself talks abut his bad experiences of temptation, pain, unanswered prayer, persecution and relationship breakdown.

It seems logical that the essense of Romans 8:28 is that God in his wisdom and love is able to turn even bad things that happen to us, as a result of human sin and the fallen world that we live in, into something that is good for us.

7. Be sensitive to the fact that for some people painful experiences are a present reality, and sometimes we will not understand why things happen in this life or how they can possibly be turned to good.

8. These six words may include: foreknew, predestined, conformed, called, justified, glorified.

There is not enough space or time to fully unpack the theological challenges these words involve. It has to be enough to say here that in this chapter of Romans, Paul's aim is to encourage believers who are either facing or about to face suffering and persecution that God is with them. These ideas were given as encouraging truths to cling to no matter what earthly challenges faced these believers.

Foreknew	God has known all about us from the beginning of the world.
Predestined	God pre-planned for us to be part of his family.
Conformed	God has worked in us so that we are becoming more like Christ.
Called	God invited us to be part of his mission.
Justified	God does not count our sins against us any more.
Glorified	we will be honoured with Jesus at the end of time.

9. We often focus on what we have failed to do for God, instead of on what God has actually done for us. Pray for one another.

WORSHIP

Make sure everyone can see a copy of the Trinitarian liturgy. Explain that you are going to read the leader part and that they should be ready to respond to the group prayer parts. They may need some time to prepare their ideas.

Perhaps respond to this by playing or singing *The Lord's My Shepherd*. There are various versions by Stuart Townend, Martin Smith (*Safe in your Arms*) or the traditional version by Scottish Psalter.

Session 6: Notes - "I Feel Defeated"
The Christian Life and the Victory of God

TO SET THE SCENE

Give people a few moments to read and digest John's case study then split them up into pairs and work out how they would respond to John. Expand the discussion by asking group members to relate similar experiences. Talk about the different types of persecution faced by Christians today across the globe.

DISCUSS TOGETHER

1. Encourage people to stay in their pairs and to flick through Romans and especially chapter 8 and come up with three truths they either learned for the first time or were reminded of during this 6-week study. Encourage people to use these things to form a prayer response to God. It is fine if others were grateful for the same things - take it as a confirmation of the importance of these truths for your group at this time.

2. There can be an arrogance that assumes God is always on whichever side we are on in every conflict. This is not the same as confidence in God's unchanging love and commitment whatever our circumstances. The more important question to ask is – are we on God's side? This promise is sandwiched between verses that talk about God justifying and ultimately glorifying us (verse 30) and God redeeming us and ultimately saving us (verse 32) - this can helps us gain perspective on all sorts of our present conflicts.

3. We can be confident when we pray to God, because if he saw our predicament as sinful and lost people and he didn't hold back sending his beloved Son to die a gruesome death on our behalf – can we really think that God would withhold from us anything that we genuinely need?

4. Our standing before and with God is so secure so that no one can bring any charge or condemn us or defeat us because Christ has fully paid the price through his death and resurrection. Whatever our situations, he will give us all things. Note the future tense here – he is not promising an easy life now, but he is promising victory in the future. Because we will never be defeated and can never be condemned, we can have confidence to turn to God in prayer.

One illustration that might help:

Imagine a mother who had gone into a burning building to rescue her toddler from the fire. In the process of rescuing the child the mother is terribly burnt and left with many scars. The mother manages to rescue the child and for the whole of his childhood he saw the scars and understood the great love his mother had for him. Do you think if the child was thirsty he would have any fear about asking his mother for a drink? Or if he was hungry would he have any fear of asking for food? How much more should we have no fear to approach God in prayer who did not spare his own son on our behalf?

5. See Romans 3:22-25 ; Romans 6:22-23 Romans 8:1-2 if you need some help.

6. Paul lists SEVEN things – remind your group to add their own to this list to help them see their own struggles in the context of this passage

1. Trouble
2. Hardship
3. Persecution
4. Famine
5. Nakedness
6. Danger
7. Sword

As group members identify other struggles it may be appropriate to pause, close our eyes and reflect. Perhaps the leader could bring these things to God in a prayer similar to the one below with your own group's points inserted.

> "Who shall separate us from the love of Christ? Shall [unemployment, or depression, or singleness, or infertility, or exhaustion, or bankruptcy, or bullying or disappointment]? ….
>
> No in all these things we are more than conquerors through him who loved us. For I am convinced that neither death nor life, neither angels nor demons, neither the present nor the future, nor any powers, neither height nor depth, nor anything else in all creation, will be able to separate us from the love of God that is in Christ Jesus our Lord."
>
> *Romans 8:35-39*

7. Paul is clear that trouble is a normal part of the Christian life, as are the other writers of the Bible – yet even in the trouble we face we are not separated from knowing the love of Christ. One day when Christ returns, all trouble will cease but until that day we hold on to the fact that nothing can alter God's love for us.

8. Encourage the group to look up the references to see why Jesus is the solution to all the things that might separate us from the love of God.

Death nor life?

> Jesus has defeated death. He is the resurrection and the life and we who have believed in him are baptised into a unbreakable connection

to Christ's death on our behalf and his resurrection life. Those facing sickness or bereavement may find comfort here.

Romans 6:5 and John 11:21-25

Angels nor demons?

Jesus has defeated all spiritual forces through his death and resurrection. We have nothing to fear if we are united with Christ. Those facing doubt and temptation may find comfort here.

Ephesians 6:12 and Philippians 2:5-11

Present nor future nor any powers?

Jesus is the same yesterday, today and forever. We know that when he is revealed in glory at the end of history we who are joined to him through faith will get to experience that glory displayed in our lives. Those facing up to past hurts, or anxieties about the future may find comfort here.

Romans 8:18 and Hebrews 13:8

Height nor depth nor anything else in all creation?

Jesus is the creator of everything that exists; creation exists to serve him so there is nothing that can ultimately harm us if we are united by faith to Christ. Those facing relationship breakdowns or concerned about global disasters may find comfort here.

Colossians 1:15-18

9. Encourage the group to come up with some practical ways we can keep reminding each other that there is nothing that can separate us from the love of God. Explore times when people feel most in need of being reminded of these things.

WORSHIP

As you read through Psalm 16, note all the connections between the Psalm and Romans 8. Response songs that may help our time of reflection include:

One Thing Remains (Your Love Never Fails) by Brian Johnson, Christa Black Gifford & Jeremy Riddle

or

Nothing Ever (Could Separate Us) by Ben Calhoun, Jason Ingram & Seth Mosley

Alternatively sing *In Christ Alone* by Stuart Townend & Keith Getty

Use Romans 8:37-39 as a pattern of prayer to proclaim trust in Christ that his victory will be revealed in those areas we struggle most with. Alternatively review the great truths that have stood out for you from each of the sessions and finish with a declaration of faith in him.

OTHER TITLES IN THE SPRING HARVEST BIBLE STUDIES SERIES:

Daniel – Faith Under Fire
Daniel's faith was literally tested by fire, but his God – and our God – proves himself faithful in the most extreme of situations.
SHB1351B

Passion – Finding An Unshakeable Hope
Exploring the significance of the cross and resurrection for our lives, hopes and relationships will help us grow in confidence and in the character and grace of God.
SHB1319B

Yahweh – God In All His Fullness
7 studies which seek to guide you into a deeper grasp of the magnificence of God.
SHB1389B

Ephesians - United
6 sessions that reflect on the church and living a Christ-inspired lifestyle.
SHB1739B

1 John
Get close to the Source in being, saying and doing.
SHB1839B